Dinosaur Valley
Activity Fun Stickers

Written by Brenda Apsley

Designed and illustrated by Cr

EGMONT
We bring stories to life

First published in Great Britain 2004 by Egmont UK Limited
239 Kensington High Street, London W8 6SA
This edition published 2011
© 2011 Egmont UK Limited
All rights reserved.
ISBN 978 1 4052 5716 9
1 3 5 7 9 10 8 6 4 2
Printed in China

It's the start of a new day in Dinosaur Valley. Draw a big sun in the sky, talk about what you can see, and colour the picture. You can add some stickers, too.

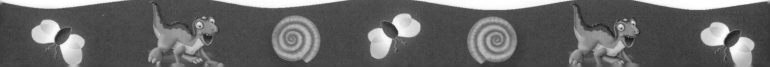

These dinosaur pictures look the same, but 5 things are different in picture 2. Can you spot all 5 differences?

Which piece will complete the jigsaw puzzle picture? Draw it in, then colour the picture.

Look very carefully! Which of these dinosaurs is different from the rest?
Colour the odd one out.

①

②

③

④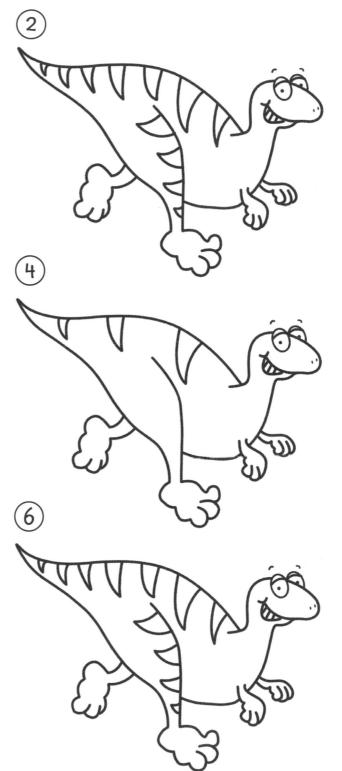

⑤

⑥

Answer: 4 is different, as he has less stripes.

Can you find and colour in 6 bones hidden in Dinosaur Desert?

The baby dinosaurs are playing a game of marbles.
Draw lines to match the numbers to the sets of marbles.

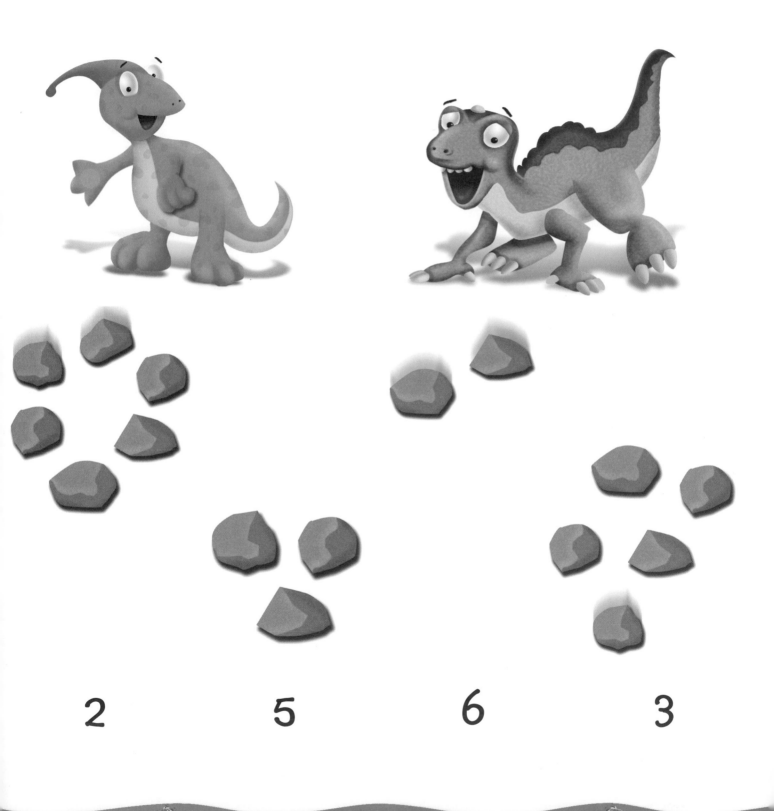

2   5   6   3

A new dinosaur has come to Dinosaur Valley. Join the dots to complete him, then colour the picture.

Use the little picture as a guide to help you colour the big one.

The fireflies are making the dinosaur dizzy! Draw more, so there are 10 altogether.

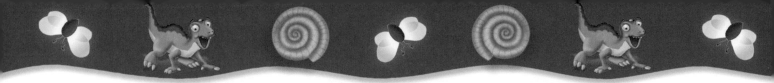

There's a big storm coming to Dinosaur Valley! Draw lots of grey thunder clouds, rain drops and flashes of lightning, then colour the picture.

Try drawing this dinosaur without taking your pencil off the paper.
Start at the dot and follow the arrow. Now, colour your drawing.

Colour the dinosaurs in order of size. Colour the smallest one green, the medium one yellow, and the biggest one brown.

Where is the baby dinosaur going? Follow the maze to find out.

Some dinosaur babies hatch from eggs. Put the pictures below in the right order by writing the numbers 1, 2, 3 and 4 in the circles under each box.

Draw lines to join the correct dinosaur heads, bodies and tails, then colour them in.

 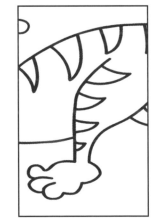 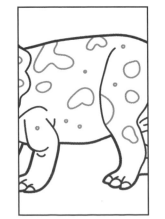

 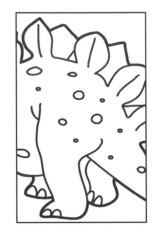 

  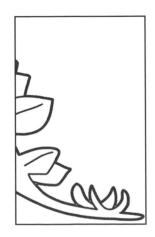

Dino and Dina, the dinosaur twins, are exactly alike. Can you find them in the herd, and colour them?

Some dinosaurs can fly. Count the number of each colour, and write the numbers on the clouds.

Colour the rest of the picture as neatly as you can. Why not add some stickers, too?

Look at the little boxes below the big picture. Tick the things you can see in the big picture.

Zzzzzz! This sleepy dinosaur is fast asleep. Draw and colour what you think he's dreaming of. Add some stickers too, if you like.

Some dinosaurs have teeth and some have spikes. Some have both.
Count each dinosaur's teeth and spikes, and write the numbers.

① teeth

spikes

② teeth

spikes

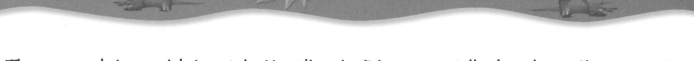

There are lots and lots of butterflies in Dinosaur Valley! Colour, then count them, and circle the number you think there are.

| 9 | 10 | 11 | 12 | 13 |

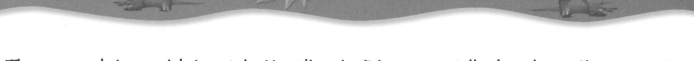

Answer: there are 12 butterflies.

Dinosaurs live on land or in the sea. Complete the sea picture as neatly as you can.

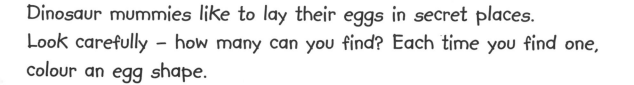

Dinosaur mummies like to lay their eggs in secret places.
Look carefully – how many can you find? Each time you find one,
colour an egg shape.

Draw your own picture of this dinosaur. It's easy if you do it piece by piece. When your drawing is complete, colour it as neatly as you can, and write your name on the line.

My dinosaur picture, by _____

Using a blue pencil, colour only the shapes with a dot in them.
You'll find someone hiding!

The baby dinosaur is looking at himself in the swamp. Which picture shows his reflection?

① ② ③ ④

It's night-time in Dinosaur Valley. Draw lines to match the dinosaurs to their shadows.

Draw some silly dinosaurs. On a piece of paper, draw a head, fold the paper so it is hidden, and pass to a friend to draw the body and legs. Fold the paper, pass it on, and draw a tail. Then open up the paper to see your Sillysaurus!

Here are two examples of how your silly dinosaur might look.

Sometimes Dinosaur Valley is a dangerous place to be. The volcano is erupting! Draw lots of smoke clouds, red, yellow and orange flames, and colour the picture. You can add stickers if you like.

This dinosaur has a big flap on his back. It helps him to keep cool. Complete it by drawing lines to connect the sets of dots, then colour the picture.

Draw lines to match the dinosaurs to the footprints they have made in the mud.

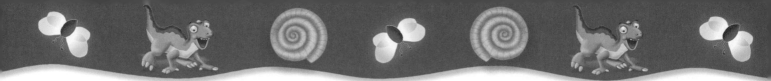

This dinosaur is very thirsty. She needs a drink of water.
Show her which path leads to the pond.

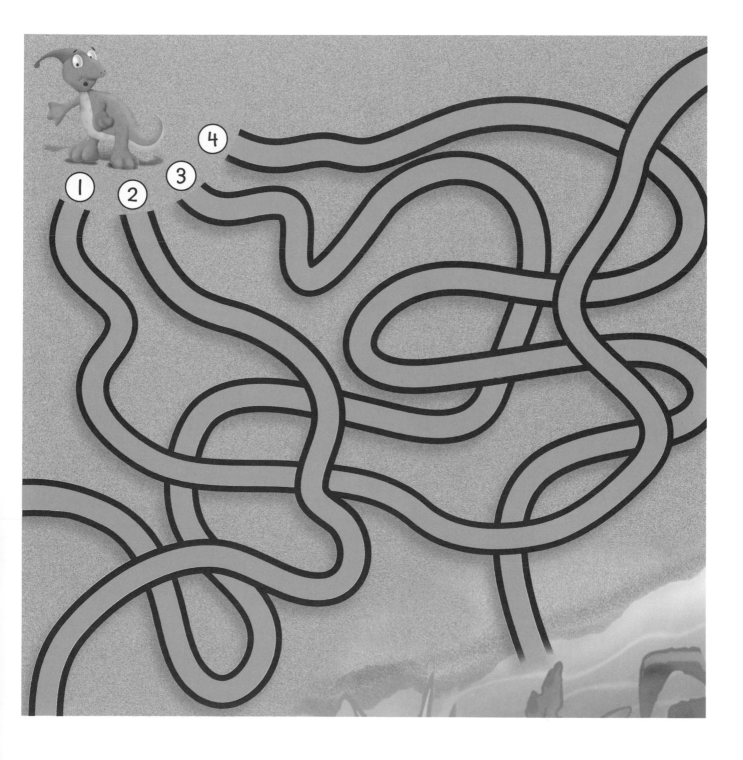

These pictures look the same, but 5 things are different in picture 2.
Can you spot the differences?

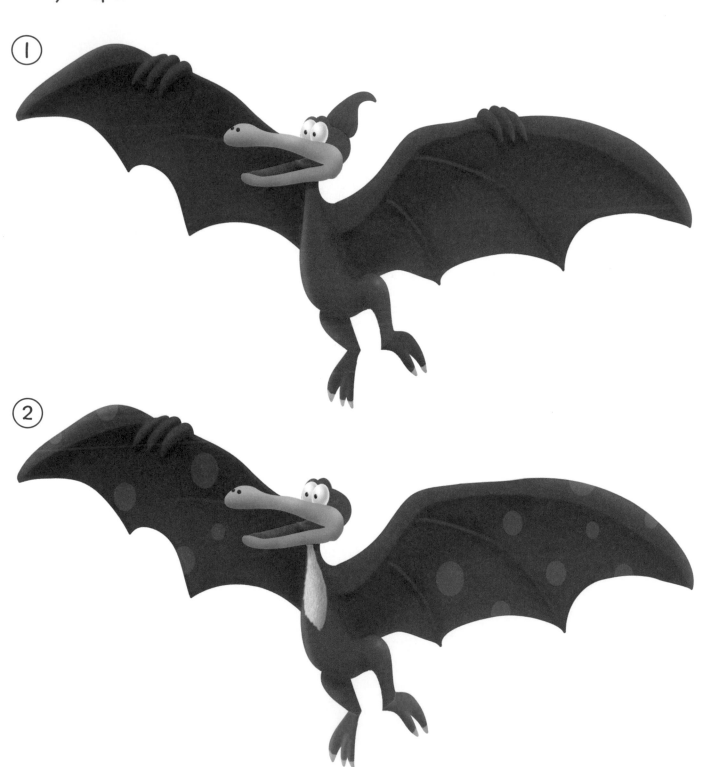

①

②

This dinosaur is very shy. He wants somewhere to hide. Draw and colour lots more spiky trees, bushes, rocks and tall grasses to hide him. You can add stickers, too.

Draw more dinosaur eggs so there are 10 in each nest.

Count the number of each thing you can *see*, and write numbers on the boulders. The first one has been done for you.

 4

Complete the picture using the colour guide. Why not add some stickers, too?

Some dinosaurs have horns. Join the dots to complete this one, starting at number 1.

Colour ONLY the things you might *see* in Dinosaur Valley.

Draw and colour the missing parts of these dinosaurs.

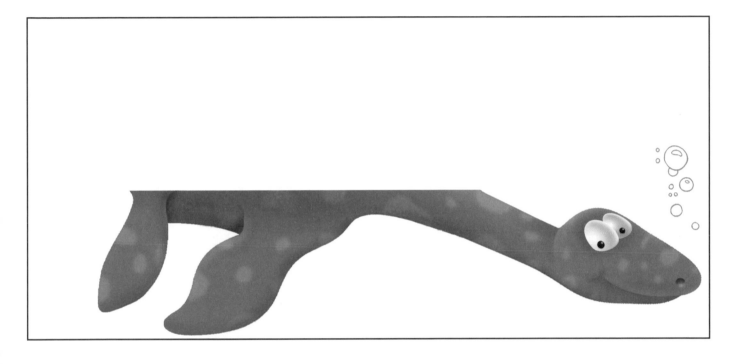

These pictures tell a story. Talk about pictures 1, 2 and 3, and draw what happens in number 4. Now, complete the pictures as neatly as you can, and tell the story in your own words. Don't forget to make lots of scary dinosaur noises!

1

2

3

4

Poor baby dinosaur! He's sad because he has no one to play rock football with. Draw and colour a friend for him. Or add a sticker!

This big family of dinosaurs all look alike, but one of them is different. Can you find and colour him?

It's night-time in Dinosaur Valley. Draw a yellow moon, lots of stars, and colour the picture. You can add some stickers if you like. Goodnight, dinosaurs!